123 SESAME STREET

Holiday Crafts

First published by Parragon in 2009

Parragon
Queen Street House
4 Queen Street
Bath BA1 1HE, UK

ISBN 978-1-4075-7195-9

Printed in China

SESAME STREET®

123

Holiday Crafts

PaRragon

Bath New York Singapore Hong Kong Cologne Delhi Melbourne

TIPS FOR SUCCESS

Prepare your space

Cover your workspace with newspaper or a plastic or paper tablecloth. Make sure you and your children are wearing clothes (including shoes!) that you don't mind becoming spattered with food, paint, or glue. But relax! You'll never completely avoid mess; in fact, it's part of the fun!

Wash your hands

Wash your hands (and your child's hands) before starting a new project, and clean up as you go along. Clean hands make for clean crafts! Remember to wash your hands afterward, too, using soap and warm water to get off any of the remaining materials.

Follow steps carefully

Follow each step carefully, and in the sequence in which it appears. We've tested all the projects; we know they work, and we want them to work for you, too. Also, ask your children, if they are old enough, to read along with you as you work through the steps. For a younger child, you can direct her to look at the pictures on the page to try to guess what the next step is.

Measure precisely

If a project gives you measurements, use your ruler, T-square, measuring cups, or measuring spoons to make sure you measure as accurately as you can. Sometimes the success of the project may depend on it. Also, this is a great opportunity to teach measuring techniques to your child.

Be patient

You may need to wait while something bakes or leave paint, glue, or clay to dry, sometimes for a few hours or even overnight. Encourage your child to be patient as well; explain to her why she must wait, and, if possible, find ways to entertain her as you are waiting. For example you can show her how long you have to wait by pointing out the time on a clock.

Clean up

When you've finished your project, clean up any mess. Store all the materials together so that they are ready for the next time you want to craft. Ask your child to help.

YOU WILL NEED

- Thin cardboard 10 x 8 inches
- Colored markers
- Glitter
- White glue and brush
- Scissors
- Tissue paper (cut into thin strips)
- Colored paper (2 colors)
- Adhesive tape
- Two sticks

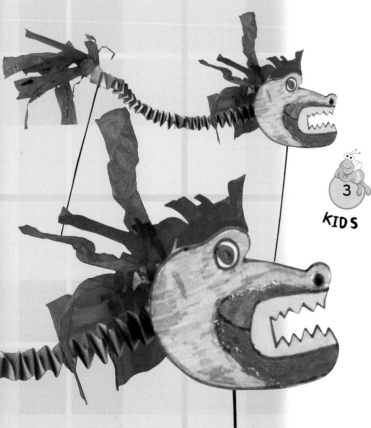

①

Draw a dragon's head onto thin cardboard. Use colored markers to color it in, then decorate it using glue and glitter.

②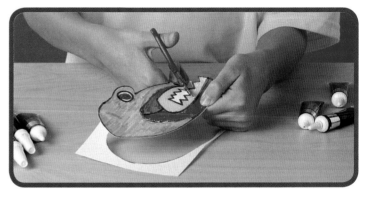

Carefully cut out the dragon's head.

3

KIDS

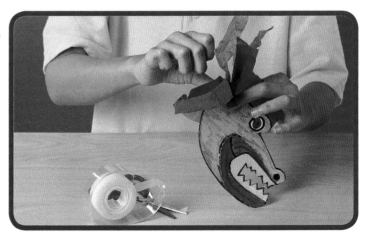

Tape half the strips of tissue paper to the back of the dragon's head.

(4)

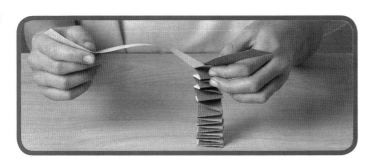

Cut two long, thin strips of colored paper the same length. Glue one to the other to make an "L" shape. Fold the yellow strip over the top of the pink strip and crease it. Then fold the pink strip down over the yellow. Continue until you can glue down the final fold.

5
KIDS

Glue the rest of the tissue paper to the dragon's tail. Glue the head to the other end of the body.

(6)

Use tape to attach the two sticks to the body – one at the head end, the other at the tail end.

DID YOU KNOW?
Chinese New Year is celebrated with a big parade. At the end of it, a dragon dances to the sound of drums, horns, and gongs!

Chinese New Year is a SUPER holiday!

VALENTINE COOKIES

YOU WILL NEED

- Large mixing bowl
- Wooden spoon
- Rolling pin
- Heart-shaped cookie cutter
- Baking sheet
- Plastic wrap
- $2\frac{1}{3}$ cups flour
- 1 teaspoon baking powder
- 1 teaspoon vanilla
- 1 stick margarine
- 1 cup soft brown sugar
- 3 tablespoons light corn syrup
- 1 egg
- Frosting
- Candy hearts and sprinkles (optional)

①

Place the flour, baking powder, vanilla, and sugar in a bowl. Add the margarine. Mix with your fingertips until the mixture is crumbly.

②

Add the syrup; mix together. Stir in the egg and mix. Turn out the mixture onto a lightly floured surface and knead it until it forms a smooth dough. Cover with plastic wrap and chill for two hours.

③

Roll out the dough on a floured surface to about one quarter of an inch. Cut out the cookies with a heart-shaped cutter. Place them on a greased baking sheet and bake at 325°F for 10 minutes. Ask an adult to help you use the oven.

4
KIDS

When the cookies are done, have an adult take them out of the oven. Leave to stand. They will harden up as they cool. When they are cool, decorate the cookies with frosting, and add some candy hearts if you wish.

DID YOU KNOW?
Valentine's Day is a great time to show people you care.

Elmo uses food coloring to make pink and red frosting. Elmo thinks these are the foods of love!

EASTER NESTS

YOU WILL NEED

- Shredded breakfast cereal
- 1 large and 1 small bowl
- Melted chocolate
- Spoon
- Foil or muffin cups
- Muffin pan
- White mint candies or yogurt-covered raisins

1

Line a muffin pan with foil or use muffin cups.

2
KIDS

Crumble the cereal into the large bowl. Check that there are no large chunks. Ask a grown-up to melt the chocolate in the small bowl.

3
KIDS

Stir the chocolate into the crumbled cereal and mix well with the spoon.

DID YOU KNOW?
Easter eggs are a symbol of new life and springtime.

Place a spoonful of the mixture into each space and press it down into a nest shape. Leave the shapes to harden in a cool, dry place. Put them on a plate and add a few white mint candies to each one.

Decorate your plate with colorful paper streamers and daffodils to make it look really spring-like.

YOU WILL NEED

- Rectangle of felt 10 x 12 inches
- Scraps of colored felt
- Ribbon long enough to fit around the felt rectangle
- Glue
- Pencil or marker pen
- Scissors
- Sequins

1 KIDS

Glue four pieces of ribbon around the edge of the felt rectangle. Tuck the ends underneath, and glue in place.

②

Draw out the letters to spell "MATZAH" onto pieces of colored felt. Cut out the letters. Fold the felt 'A's in half for an easy way to cut out the holes.

DID YOU KNOW?
Matzah has just two ingredients—flour and water!

MATZAH

Glue the letters onto the felt background. Decorate with felt shapes and sequins.

MATZAH

Your Matzah cover is now ready to use.

MOM'S PHOTO WALLET

YOU WILL NEED

- Thick cardboard
- Scissors
- Paper
- Glue
- Ribbon
- Pretty pictures from magazines
- Photographs

1 You will need two equal-sized pieces of thick cardboard for the cover. Glue them onto colored paper, as shown, leaving a gap between them.

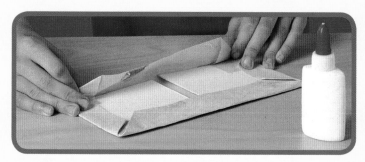

2 Fold in the colored paper neatly and firmly, then glue it down, so that the outer edges of the two pieces of cardboard are completely covered.

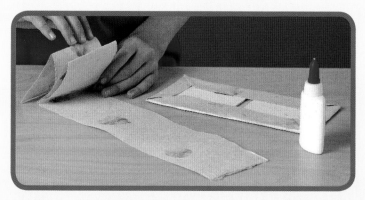

3 Take a long piece of colored paper and fold it back and forth as if you are making a fan. This will make the pages of the wallet.

4
KIDS

Glue a piece of ribbon to the inside of both cardboard covers, down the middle, and leave to dry. This will tie in a bow to keep your wallet closed.

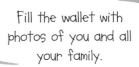

DID YOU KNOW? Mother's Day is celebrated in many countries around the world.

Fill the wallet with photos of you and all your family.

5

Glue one end of the folded page section to the inside front cover. It should cover the ribbon, too. Glue the other end to the inside back cover.

6
KIDS

Decorate the front cover with ribbon and a picture of something pretty cut from a magazine.

FATHER'S DAY

YOU WILL NEED

- Wooden doorknob
- Oven-bake clay
- Glue
- Paintbrush
- Varnish
- Paint

1

Make some miniature tools from oven-bake clay, and bake them in the oven according to the manufacturer's instructions.

2

KIDS

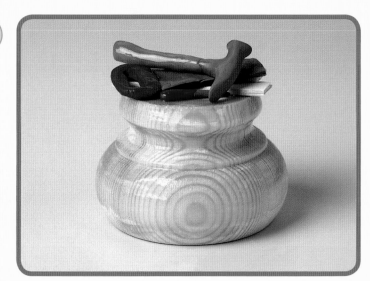

Glue the hardened tools to the top of the doorknob. When the glue is dry, varnish the doorknob and the tools, and leave to dry. Your Father's Day paperweight is finished.

DID YOU KNOW?
Many countries around the world have a Father's Day, honoring fathers, grandfathers, and uncles.

Try out different designs. If your father loves golfing, decorate one with a golf ball and tee. You could even paint the doorknob green for the golf course.

Choose decorations that suit your father's personality or hobbies.

USA WREATH

YOU WILL NEED

- Large paper plate
- Scissors
- Pencil
- Ruler
- 1 x 4-inch strips of red and blue paper
- Adhesive tape
- White paper
- Gluestick
- Thin white ribbon
- Glitter glue (optional)

①

Draw and cut out a circle from the middle of the paper plate, leaving an even border all the way round, about two inches wide.

KIDS

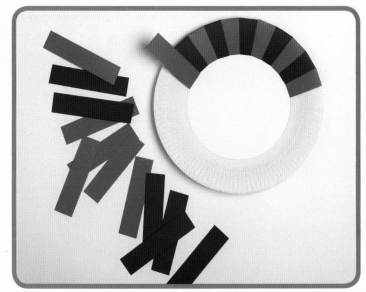

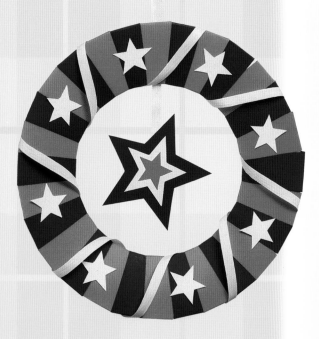

For the next step, you will need lots of strips of red and blue paper. Wrap them around the plate in stripes. Tape them on the back as you go.

③

Cut out white stars and glue them around the edge. Twist the thin white ribbon around the wreath. Secure on the back with tape.

④

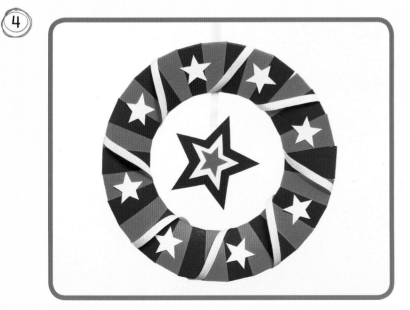

Cut out a blue star, and stick a smaller white and red star in the center. Tape it to the wreath with ribbon, so it hangs down. Add a long loop of ribbon to hang up your wreath.

You can decorate the white stars with glitter glue to make them sparkly.

EID DECORATIONS

①

Draw a crescent moon and a star onto a paper plate. Cut them out.

②

Cut out pieces of foil slightly bigger than the moon and star. Cover the moon and star with foil, neatly folding in the edges as shown.

3

KIDS

DID YOU KNOW? Eid-ul-Fitr is a time for giving and sharing. It celebrates the end of the Muslim fast of Ramadan.

Hang your moon and star by an open window, so it can twirl and sparkle in the breeze.

Brush glue all along the edges of the moon and star, then sprinkle with glitter. Leave to dry.

4

Use glittery thread to hang the star from the moon, as shown. Tie a longer thread to the top of the moon, so it can be hung from the ceiling.

21

PUMPKIN FUN!

YOU WILL NEED

- Pumpkin (any size)
- Black marker pen
- Knife
- Tealight

1 **KIDS** Use a black marker pen to draw a face onto one side of your pumpkin. You can draw triangles for the eyes and nose, and a jagged strip for the mouth, if you like.

2 Ask an adult to cut a circle around the top of the pumpkin for the lid, and the holes for the eyes, nose, and mouth.

3 Place a tealight inside the pumpkin so it can shine through the holes. Ask a grown-up to light it for you.

NAPKIN RINGS

YOU WILL NEED

- Cardboard tube
- Scissors
- Pencil or marker pen
- White glue and brush
- Tissue paper strips
- Foil candy wrappers torn into strips

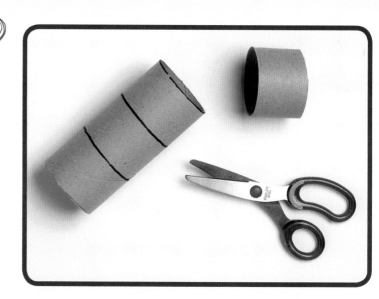

Mark sections about one inch wide on the cardboard tube, as shown, then carefully cut the tube into sections.

2 KIDS

Brush glue all over the outside and inside of each ring. Wrap tissue paper strips around them, brushing on more glue to help them stick. Glue foil strips over the tissue strips for a sparkly effect.

Touch up with glue in spots that need it, then leave to dry. Roll up a napkin and push it into a ring, then put at table setting.

DID YOU KNOW?
Long ago, instead of using napkins, people wiped their hands on a slice of bread.

Napkins are handy for sticky desserts!

QUIET CRACKERS

YOU WILL NEED

- Cardboard tubes
- Tissue or crêpe paper rectangles (3 times as long as tubes and wide enough to overlap)
- White glue and brush
- Adhesive tape
- Foil and colorful paper
- Candies, small gifts, and confetti

 1 KIDS

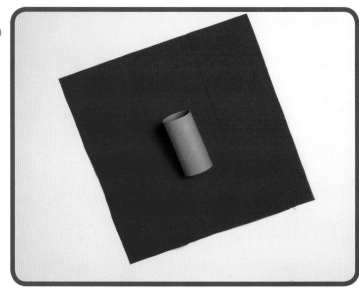

Place a cardboard tube in the middle of a large rectangle of tissue or crêpe paper.

2 KIDS

Roll the paper around the tube, secure it with tape, then twist it at one end to close it. Push candies, confetti, and a small gift into the tube.

3
KIDS

Twist the other end of the cracker to close it, then decorate the cracker with festive decorations.

4
KIDS

Make a lot of different colored crackers, one for each guest at your holiday party. You could even put a name on each one.

DID YOU KNOW?
The first crackers were just like the ones here, but later, the inventor added a loud POP!

You could also write your favorite jokes on small strips of paper, and put one in each cracker.

MENORAH CANDLES

YOU WILL NEED

- Pack air-drying clay
- Modeling tool
- Rolling pin
- Pencil
- Acrylic paints
- Paintbrush
- Glitter
- Candles (birthday cake candles work well)

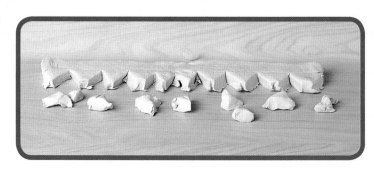

1 Divide the clay in half. Roll out one half into a long rectangle, about one inch thick. Cut a **zigzag** along one edge for the base of the menorah. Flatten all the points slightly so that it will stand up. Then use the modeling tool to cut the base into three sections: two with four points, and one with two points.

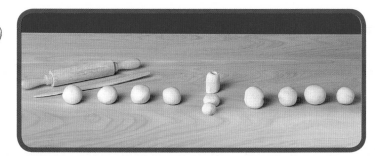

2 Divide up the remaining clay into balls. Roll eleven into short sausage shapes for the candleholders—three for the center and four on each side. Make holes for the candles with a pencil.

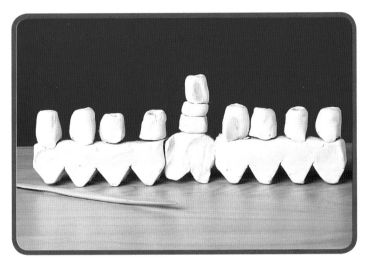

Use the modeling tool to assemble the menorah. Leave it to dry in a warm, airy place before decorating it.

4
KIDS

Decorate the menorah with paint and glitter, and let dry. Ask an adult to help you use it during the eight nights of Hanukkah. The center, or leader, candle, is used to light one more candle each night, until they are all lit on the last night.

DID YOU KNOW?
Hanukkah is the Jewish Festival of Lights. It lasts for eight days and nights in the wintertime.

KWANZAA HAT

YOU WILL NEED

- Thin cardboard: black, green, red
- Scissors
- Pencil
- Ruler
- Glue or adhesive tape

Cut a strip of thin black cardboard two inches wide by twenty-four inches long. Cut a thinner strip of green cardboard the same length. Decorate by gluing bits of red and black paper on the green strip.

2 KIDS

Glue the green strip in the middle of the black strip, as shown. Overlap the ends of the band and tape them together to fit around your head.

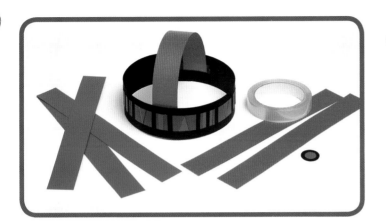

Cut three red and three green strips, one inch wide by twelve inches long. Bend one of them across the inside of the headband and stick down both ends.

4

KIDS

Do the same with the other five strips, so they are evenly spaced as shown. Cut out a small round circle and glue it on the top to finish your Kwanzaa hat.

DID YOU KNOW?
Kwanzaa is a week-long African-American holiday in December. It celebrates family, community, and culture.

Hey!
I'm Kwanzaa-colored!
Now scram!

INDEX